quick TESTS

Spelling

7-8 YEARS

Key Stage 2

Wendy Bloom

WHSmith Spelling Quick Tests

- Spelling key words is central to National Curriculum English for all primary-age children.
- Key words are also a prominent feature of the National Literacy Framework, implemented in all schools from September 1998.
- We have produced this series of tests to help build your child's confidence and ability in spelling.
- Early practice and testing in spelling will provide your child with a good foundation in reading and writing – essential for future success.

How you can help

- At Key Stage 2 (ages 8–11), your child is expected to:
  - remember the spellings of more complex words;
  - recognise and spell correctly a widening variety of letter combinations;
  - identify and write common prefixes and suffixes;
  - recognise common spelling patterns;
  - know common spelling rules.

The following will help your child to improve his or her spelling.

- Get your child to *write* the words, not just 'sound them out'.
- Get your child to learn the sounds made by letters and groups of letters.
- Make sure your child has regular practice with irregular, well-used words.
- Make words with magnetic or plastic letters.
- Get your child to write each word often, with different writing tools on different surfaces.
- Look for words in books, magazines and newspapers, and in everyday situations (at home, at the shops, on TV).

How to use this book

This book includes:

- examples of words with common letter strings, prefixes (beginnings), roots, suffixes (endings) and sounds;
- spelling rules;
- lists of most-used words to learn and check;
- revision pages to practise words already learnt.

A few simple guidelines will ensure that your child gets the best from this book.

- Do some spelling work once or twice a week, in 20–30 minute sessions.
- Agree on a set time with your child, and keep it the same if possible.
- Give your child a piece of plain card to cover the words.
- If your child is finding it difficult, slow the pace. Together you could make up ways to help your child remember more complex words, for example 'Wed/nes/day'.
- If your child knows the words very well already, either spend more time on the activities or move on to the next group of words.
- Praise and encourage your child at all stages.

How to use this spelling book

1. Read the writing at the top of the page.
2. Say the words aloud. Ask someone to help you if you like.
3. Look at the first word on the list.
4. Cover the other words with your cover card.
5. Look very carefully at the word. What groups of letters are at the beginning, middle and end?
6. Say the word slowly. If it is a long word, split it up into parts (syllables).
7. Close your eyes and think about the word.
8. Cover the word with your cover card.
9. Write the word in the *Try it here* column. Say the word as you write it. (After the first time, the two columns don't have these headings. But remember, that is what you do.)
10. Check the word.
    - Is it right? Tick it and go on to the next word.
    - Not quite right? Cover it, then write it again in the *Try it again* column. Check it again.
    - Still not quite right? Go to page 31 and copy it into the *My words* column.

Don't forget … keep practising all your words!

Three ways of writing the *or* sound

Same sound, different letters.

1	for	sport	forty	torn
Try it here	________	________	________	________
Try it again	________	________	________	________

2	law	claw	lawn	straw
Try it here	________	________	________	________
Try it again	________	________	________	________

3	caught	August
Try it here	____________	____________
Try it again	____________	____________

List 2

Three ways of writing the *er* sound

Same sound, different spelling again.

1	her	were	herd
	______	______	______
	______	______	______

2	sir	third	bird
	______	______	______
	______	______	______

3 turn	burn	mur/der	urg/ent
______	______	______	______
______	______	______	______

Spelling the months

Check the months of the year.

Can you spell them all?

Jan/u/ary	**July**
Feb/ru/ary	**August**
March	**September**
April	**Oc/to/ber**
May	**No/vem/ber**
June	**De/cem/ber**

List 4

The sound *ear*

Here are two different ways to spell the sound *ear*.

See if you can sort them out.

1 **fear** **hearing** **clear**

__________ __________ __________

near **gear**

__________ __________

2 **deer** (animal) **cheer**

__________ __________

steering **beer** **veer**

__________ __________ __________

Words you need to know

Here is a list of words you will want to use often in your writing. Check that you can spell them accurately.

	Try it here	*Try it again*
been (I have …)	______________	______________
boy	______________	______________
back	______________	______________
because	______________	______________
school	______________	______________
house	______________	______________
many	______________	______________
more	______________	______________
about	______________	______________
again	______________	______________

Choose four words and write a sentence for each one.

The sound *ea*

Here are two different ways of writing the sound *ea* (as in d*ea*d).

1 **head** **ready** **spread**

________ ________ ________

steady **weather**

________ ________

2 **never** **well** **wedding**

________ ________ ________

shed **spell**

________ ________

Underline the *ea* sound in each word.

Fill in the missing words

sport **caught** **third** **burn**

August **hear** **school** **cheering**

because **weather**

Complete these sentences using words from the box above.

1 Which s__________ can you play in s__________?

2 Be careful of sun__________ in A__________ .

3 John c__________ a cold in the bad w__________ .

4 I can h__________ the c__________ b__________ we won the t__________ prize!

List 7

Looking back and making sure

A quick look back over some vowel sounds.

name ______________ ______________

flame ______________ ______________

plate ______________ ______________

whale ______________ ______________

make ______________ ______________

liked ______________ ______________

strike ______________ ______________

white ______________ ______________

tide ______________ ______________

stride ______________ ______________

More vowel sounds

Can you remember these vowel sounds?

high ____________ ____________

sigh ____________ ____________

flight ____________ ____________

tight ____________ ____________

night ____________ ____________

fly ____________ ____________

try ____________ ____________

sty ____________ ____________

why ____________ ____________

cry ____________ ____________

More to remember

Can you still spell these words?

goat ______________ ______________

loaded ______________ ______________

boating ______________ ______________

floating ______________ ______________

soaking ______________ ______________

owing ______________ ______________

showing ______________ ______________

blowing ______________ ______________

flowing ______________ ______________

mowing ______________ ______________

Choose four words and write a sentence for each one.

Double trouble

Here we look at double consonants in words.

bb		*tt*	
bubble	________	**butter**	________
wobble	________	**little**	________
rubber	________	**bottle**	________
nibble	________	**shuttle**	________
chubby	________	**better**	________

Can you think of any more?

________ ________ ________ ________

________ ________ ________ ________

________ ________ ________ ________

More doubles

Here are some more double consonants.

dd		*ff*	
middle	________	**cliff**	________
riddle	________	**sniff**	________
cuddled	________	**shuffle**	________
muddy	________	**waffles**	________
toddler	________	**baffled**	________

Can you think of any more?

________ ________ ________ ________

________ ________ ________ ________

________ ________ ________ ________

Fill in the missing letters

Can you remember how to spell these words?

name **cry** **white** **night**

middle **high** **make**

butter **soak** **stride**

Finish off these words. Cover up the words above.

n_m_ wh_t_

m_k_ str_d_

hi___ ni___t

cr_ s___k

bu_____r mi_____e

More words to remember

Make sure of these words.

They often come up in reading and writing.

brother ______________ ______________

after ______________ ______________

another ______________ ______________

good ______________ ______________

girl ______________ ______________

first ______________ ______________

laugh ______________ ______________

night ______________ ______________

next ______________ ______________

half ______________ ______________

Choose four words and write a sentence for each one.

More doubles

Here are some more double consonants.

ll		*ss*	
full	________	**dress**	________
falling	________	**messy**	________
smaller	________	**glass**	________
still	________	**missed**	________
smelly	________	**fussy**	________

Can you think of any more?

________ ________ ________ ________

________ ________ ________ ________

________ ________ ________ ________

Even more double consonants

This is the last group of double consonants.

rr		*mm*	
worry	________	**mummy**	________
hurry	________	**tummy**	________
furry	________	**hammer**	________
lorry	________	**stammer**	________
sorry	________	**humming**	________

Can you think of any more?

________ ________ ________ ________

________ ________ ________ ________

________ ________ ________ ________

Words with *ck*

Very few English words end with *c* or *k* on their own or have a *c* or *k* alone in the middle.

luck	__________	**bucket**	__________
stick	__________	**wicket**	__________
neck	__________	**wicked**	__________
lick	__________	**jacket**	__________
back	__________	**sacked**	__________

Can you think of any more?

__________ __________ __________ __________

__________ __________ __________ __________

__________ __________ __________ __________

Words with *ph*

ph in a word sounds like an *f*.

Try these out. Say each word aloud, clearly.

phone ____________ ____________

elephant ____________ ____________

photo ____________ ____________

graph ____________ ____________

photograph ____________ ____________

phoneme ____________ ____________

phantom ____________ ____________

phew! ____________ ____________

alphabet ____________ ____________

phrase ____________ ____________

Complete these sentences

Here are some clues. Write the missing words in these sentences. Check each word carefully.

1 I'm his sister, he's my ______________ .

2 You're so funny, you make me ______________ .

3 Sleep well – good______________ .

4 I'm bigger than you, you're ______________ than me.

5 Please put your things away, this room is so ___________ .

6 I didn't mean to hurt you, I'm so ______________ .

7 My ______________ is coming to fetch us from school.

8 Good ______________! I hope you do well.

9 Can you write all the letters in the ______________ ?

10______________! I feel really hot!

More words to remember

Make sure of these words. You often need them.

little ________________ ________________

laugh ________________ ________________

people ________________ ________________

should ________________ ________________

would ________________ ________________

can’t ________________ ________________

don’t ________________ ________________

saw ________________ ________________

what ________________ ________________

where ________________ ________________

Choose four words and write a sentence for each one.

Silent letters

Some of these letters don't make a sound, but you still have to write them.

knife __________ __________

knee __________ __________

know __________ __________

wrong __________ __________

wrinkle __________ __________

writing __________ __________

knit __________ __________

thumb __________ __________

lamb __________ __________

comb __________ __________

Underline each silent letter.

Prefixes

A prefix gives you a clue to the meaning of a word.

Pre… often means before or in advance.

prefix __________ __________

predict __________ __________

preview __________ __________

prepare __________ __________

prevent __________ __________

preserve __________ __________

presenter __________ __________

prefer __________ __________

prefect __________ __________

premium __________ __________

More prefixes

Un… at the beginning of a word often changes the main part to mean the opposite (e.g. happy/unhappy).

uncover _______________ _______________

untidy _______________ _______________

unwell _______________ _______________

unhelpful _______________ _______________

unhappy _______________ _______________

undo _______________ _______________

unable _______________ _______________

unfair _______________ _______________

unsure _______________ _______________

unsafe _______________ _______________

Prefixes again

Dis at the beginning of a word sometimes changes the meaning of the main part of the word (e.g. like/dislike).

distaste ____________ ____________

disbelieve ____________ ____________

disagree ____________ ____________

disable ____________ ____________

disarm ____________ ____________

dismiss ____________ ____________

discord ____________ ____________

discover ____________ ____________

disease ____________ ____________

distant ____________ ____________

Prefixes

The prefix *re* can mean doing something again.

replace ____________ ____________

resell ____________ ____________

recall ____________ ____________

retell ____________ ____________

remove ____________ ____________

renew ____________ ____________

repair ____________ ____________

repeat ____________ ____________

reply ____________ ____________

report ____________ ____________

Can you find any other *re* words in the dictionary?

Find the words

laugh what know thumb

predict prefer untidy

unfair dislike disagree

Cover the words up after you have looked at them carefully.

Find them in the letter square and circle them.

a	m	w	h	a	t	l	k	p	o
a	x	k	i	s	s	k	n	o	w
o	d	i	s	l	i	k	e	m	e
b	q	r	s	u	n	t	i	d	y
p	r	e	d	i	c	t	h	g	m
d	c	d	i	s	a	g	r	e	e
a	f	g	y	p	r	e	f	e	r
t	h	u	m	b	s	t	u	c	k
n	w	u	n	f	a	i	r	q	t
j	m	z	t	u	l	a	u	g	h

My words

This page is for you to make a list of words that you want to learn. Check with someone to make sure you have written them correctly.

My words	*Try them here*	*Try again*

Answers to tests

1
1. Which s***port*** can you play in s***chool***?
2. Be careful of sun***burn*** in A***ugust***.
3. John c***aught*** a cold in the bad w***eather***.
4. I can h***ear*** the c***heering*** be***cause*** we won the t***hird*** prize!

3
1. I'm his sister, he's my ***brother***.
2. You're so funny, you make me ***laugh***.
3. Sleep well – good ***night***.
4. I'm bigger than you, you're ***smaller*** than me.
5. Please put your things away, this room is so ***messy***.
6. I didn't mean to hurt you, I'm so ***sorry***.
7. My ***mummy*** is coming to fetch us from school.
8. Good ***luck***! I hope you do well.
9. Can you write all the letters in the ***alphabet***?
10. ***Phew***! I feel really hot!